CREATIVE
COLOURING

Beautiful
Patterns

First published in Great Britain in 2014
This revised edition published in 2016 by LOM ART, an imprint of
Michael O'Mara Books Limited
9 Lion Yard
Tremadoc Road
London SW4 7NQ

A CIP catalogue record for this book is available from the
British Library.

Papers used by Michael O'Mara Books Limited are natural, recyclable
products made from wood grown in sustainable forests. The
manufacturing processes conform to the environmental regulations of
the country of origin.

ISBN: 978-1-910552-46-9

1 2 3 4 5 6 7 8 9 10

www.mombooks.com

Cover designed by Billy Waqar
Cover illustration by Jo Taylor

Illustrations by Angela Porter, Greg Stevenson, Hannah Davies,
Jo Taylor, Julie Ingham, Rosalind Monks, Sally Moret and Textile Candy

Printed and bound in China

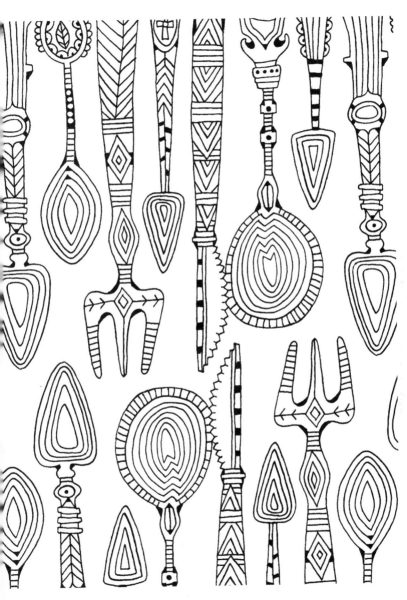